Rowdy's Big Day

Written by Cindy Robertson Waters
Illustrated by Jerry Dillingham

Printed in Guangzhou, Guangdong, China.
The DALMATIAN PRESS name is a trademark of Dalmatian Publishing Group, Franklin, Tennessee 37068-2068. 1-866-418-2572.

CE13506/1110

DalmatianPress234010958F16842264-03/11

Trent lived on a ranch where they raised horses. Lots of horses! The horses all had graceful legs, thick manes, and long, flowing tails. Trent and his family raised American quarter horses. Every year they showed their horses at the State Fair.

Trent had his own quarter horse named Rowdy. Trent was going to show Rowdy for the first time at the State Fair!

Rowdy was a warm dark brown with a black mane and tail. Trent had taken care of him ever since Rowdy was a foal, romping around in the grass with his mother.

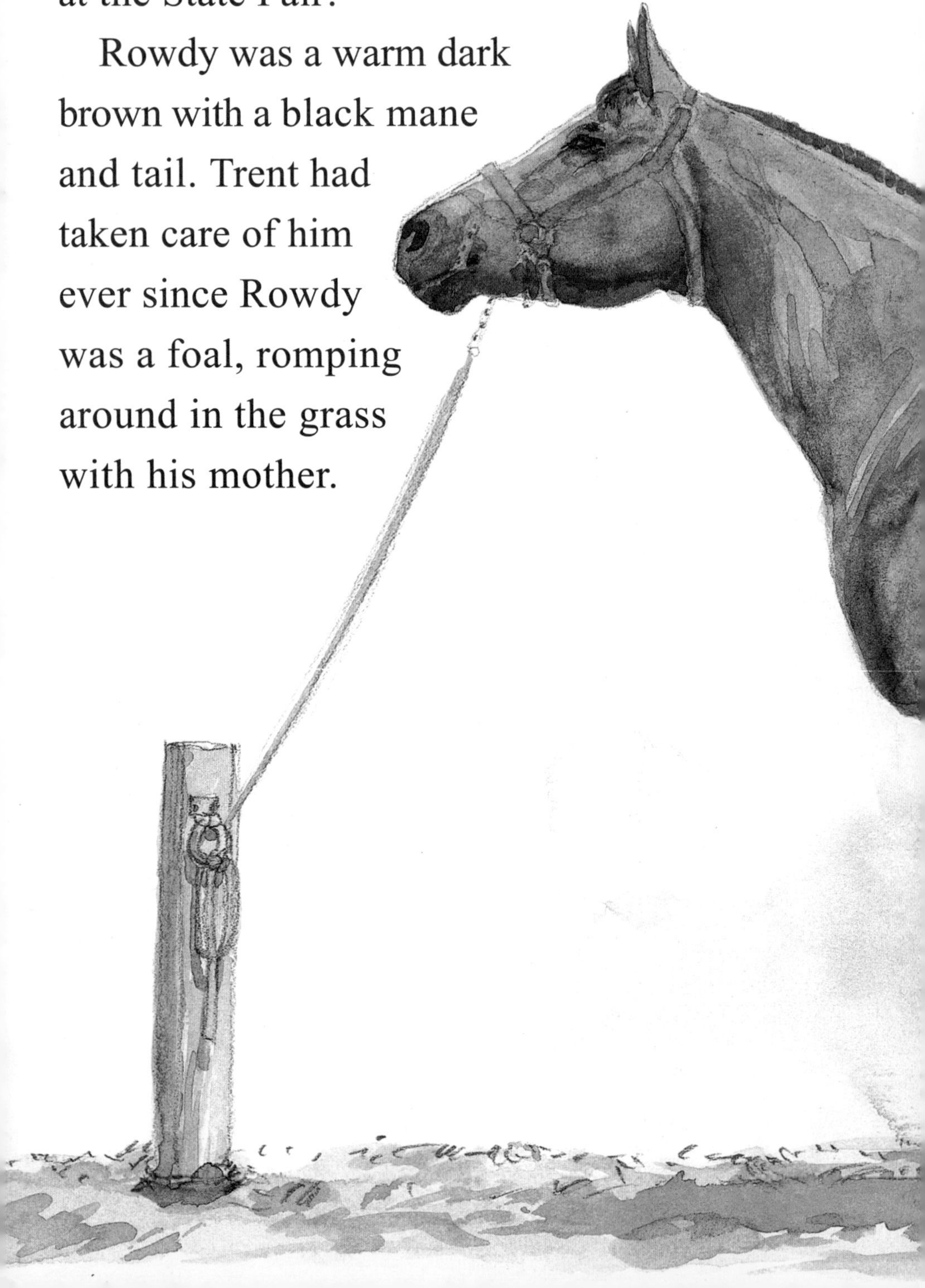

Taking care of a horse wasn't all play. Every day, Trent cleaned Rowdy's stall, groomed the horse with a comb and brush, and gave him fresh food and water.

After much hard work and preparation, the day came to carefully load Rowdy into the horse trailer…

…and Trent was off to show Rowdy in the Youth Quarter Horse Competition at the Fair—all by himself!

State Fairs were exciting! There would be wonderful foods, exhibits, and rides. And horses of all kinds!

“We’ll see big, strong horses that help plow fields and pull wagons,” Trent’s dad explained. “Those horses are called draft horses. They’re bigger than Rowdy, and they have large feet. That makes them perfect for working on a farm.”

"And there will be pony rides at the Fair, too. Children can ride the small Shetland ponies. Shetlands aren't nearly as tall or big as horses."

“One night while we’re there, I’ll take you to the circus!” said Trent’s dad. “You’ll see grand, white horses prancing around the ring—with riders standing on the horses’ backs!”

Trent was really excited about that. He could not wait to see the circus horses with their plumes and performing their tricks.

"I'll take you to the racetrack this year, too," his dad added. "You can see the harness racing. Standardbreds pull drivers around in carts called sulkies.

"Or maybe we'll go to watch the sleek racehorses carrying riders called jockeys. Those horses are thoroughbreds. They are bred to be speedy."

After a few hours on the road, Trent and his dad pulled into the fairgrounds. They unloaded Rowdy and put him in a stall in one of the big barns.

The next day, Trent went to the barn early to feed and groom Rowdy. He wanted him to look his best that night for the Youth Quarter Horse Competition.

What fun they had that evening! Trent and his dad spent hours walking around the Fair, having fun on the rides and eating cotton candy.

Finally, it was time for Rowdy's event. Trent was ready. He and his handsome quarter horse entered the big showground. Rowdy held his head high as he walked and trotted around in the spotlight.

They waited as several other horses circled the ring. And then a voice from the loudspeaker boomed:

"And the winner of the Youth Quarter Horse Competition is—Rowdy!"

Trent was so proud of Rowdy! They had taken first place! All of Rowdy's training and Trent's hard work had paid off with a big blue ribbon.

Trent would always remember Rowdy's big day at the State Fair. But he also knew that, with or without a blue ribbon, Rowdy was the **best** horse in the world.